HELP!

SOMEONE I LOVE
HAS DEMENTIA

Jo Johnson

Consulting Editor: Dr. Jim Winter

© Day One Publications 2015
First printed 2015

ISBN 978-1-84625-458-1

All Scripture quotations, unless stated otherwise,
are from the New International Version, 2011

Published by Day One Publications
Ryelands Road, Leominster, HR6 8NZ
Tel 01568 613 740   Fax 01568 611 473
North America Toll Free 888 329 6630
email—sales@dayone.co.uk
website—www.dayone.co.uk

Printed by Orchard Press (Cheltenham) Ltd

Contents

'Dementia' is a word that most people have heard and which provokes fear. Given that you have picked up this booklet it would seem reasonable to presume that you are worried about dementia, probably for a loved one, but possibly for yourself.

Few people properly understand dementia. It is in fact not a condition but a collection of symptoms resulting from many different causes, some treatable and some not. A diagnosis of dementia usually comes as a shock, even if you have been expecting it, and it is a worrying and upsetting time for the person with dementia and everyone close.

I am a neuropsychologist and also a Christian. My job includes completing pen and paper tests, often called a cognitive assessment, to see if someone has dementia. I have also been involved in supporting families and helping them to come to terms with the diagnosis of dementia. In this booklet I want to help you in the following four practical and spiritual areas:

- To give a brief overview of the facts about dementia

- To give you practical tips that will make the next few years a little easier for everyone

- To help you get the support you need from your church

- To remind and encourage you that God knows and understands your distress and will give you the wisdom you need without finding fault (James 1:5).

In this booklet you will find advice on the following topics:

- I am worried about dementia but don't have a diagnosis

- What is dementia?

- Types and causes of dementia

- Treatment for dementia

- My relative has just been diagnosed

- What do I need to do now?

- Living with dementia

- Caring for yourself

- Why is God allowing this?

Most importantly, I want to encourage you that

> *in all things God works for the good of those*
> *who love him, who have been called according*
> *to his purpose.*
>
> *(Romans 8:28)*

Thus, if you are a Bible-believing Christian, this verse assures you that God will use all things that happen to you for your good. The 'all' of this verse includes dementia. This can be hard to accept. It is easy to believe that 'all things' are working for our good when they are going well; it is harder when something bad happens—but the promise is equally true.

Understanding dementia

I am worried about dementia but don't have a diagnosis

There is great general awareness of dementia today; unfortunately this means that people sometimes become unnecessarily anxious that they or someone they love has dementia, when the problem is actually that they are too busy or stressed, or their symptoms are just part of the normal ageing process. In this first section we look at ten key symptoms that might indicate you need to consult your doctor, whether you notice them in your loved one or in yourself.

1. Significant memory problems

It is normal to sometimes forget someone's name or what we have gone into a room for. This tends to happen when we are busy and distracted by other things. However, if memory problems are beginning to disrupt life and other people are noticing, there may be a problem.

2. Problems doing everyday tasks

We all have times when we burn a meal or can't make sense of a maths problem, but if your loved one is frequently having difficulties doing things he or she always found easy—such as getting dressed, finding his or her way in familiar areas, cooking or making sense of the finances, there may be a problem.

3. Losing track of time

There are times when everyone has to think hard to remember the day of the week or what month it is, but if this happens frequently and is a struggle to figure out, it may be a sign that something is wrong.

4. Visual difficulties

Problems with eyes and vision are common as we age, but if there are difficulties making sense of visual images and problems in working out spatial relationships between objects, this may be a sign of dementia. Examples include difficulty understanding written text even when able to see the words, difficulty judging distances, or getting muddled with everyday objects, such as mistaking a cup for a bowl.

5. Making poor judgements

Poor judgements in everyday life can also develop with dementia and people can begin to make uncharacteristically bizarre, impulsive or ill-thought-out decisions. This might include giving away large sums of money or buying things that are expensive.

6. Word-finding difficulties

We all struggle at times to find the right word, but with dementia, people develop new problems with using words. They may have problems naming things—for example, calling a 'pen' an 'ink write' or a watch 'the arm time'. They may also develop more general problems with conversation, including following the thread and rules of conversation, or stopping mid-flow.

7. Losing things very often

We all lose things, but losing things and not being able to retrace our steps, or frequently finding things in odd places (a phone in the fridge, cheese in a drawer) may be a sign that something is wrong.

8. Withdrawal from social activities

If someone noticeably withdraws from activities he or she previously enjoyed, something may be wrong.

9. Getting lost

We all occasionally feel disoriented, especially in new places, but if people start to get lost in places they know well or forget how to walk or drive a familiar route, this may be cause for concern.

10. Changes in mood and personality

Significant changes in personality—such as easy-going, gentle people becoming blunt, suspicious, fearful or anxious—might indicate a problem. Dementia-related personality changes are often more pronounced when people are in unfamiliar places or situations. This is not the same as becoming 'set in your ways' and liking things to be done in a particular way.

Everybody experiences some of these problems some of the time. However, if a lot of these problems are happening on a regular basis, a doctor needs to be consulted. There is a range of conditions that can cause similar symptoms to those of dementia but which are treatable, so it is important to consult your GP to exclude them. If the diagnosis is dementia, while such a diagnosis will be difficult to hear, lots of help and support can be accessed, and living with dementia will be made easier by having early guidance.

What is dementia?

Dementia is a term used to describe a set of symptoms affecting memory and other mental skills, behaviour and mood. It is the result of changes in the brain caused by many different conditions, although the best-known is probably Alzheimer's disease. Dementia is a progressive condition, which means that symptoms get worse over time, but each individual is different and many people have several years of good-quality life after a diagnosis.

There is no straightforward test for dementia. A diagnosis is usually made by excluding other causes which present similar symptoms.

The most common symptoms are those listed above. Often it is the personality changes that are the most painful for relatives.

In the early stages, many of these symptoms can be managed by doing things differently and using strategies such as writing notes and using alarms to enable the person with dementia to continue to lead an active and independent life. Sufferers may later lose the skills they need to cope independently with day-to-day life and sometimes fail to recognize familiar faces, even of those close to them. Eventually this means that people with dementia become reliant on others for daily living. With the right advice and support, however, much can be done to help with these difficulties.

What are the different types and causes of dementia?

There are several different types of dementia. Alzheimer's disease is the most common type and the one most people have heard about. Of all the people diagnosed with dementia, just over half will have Alzheimer's. In Alzheimer's disease brain cells begin to die, affecting the structure and chemistry of the brain. We do not yet know what causes this to happen. Problems with remembering, speech and finding one's way are often the first symptoms that relatives notice.

Vascular dementia (or multi-infarct dementia) is the second most common form, accounting for about a fifth of people with dementia. It occurs when the oxygen supply to the brain is disrupted and brain cells die as a result. This may be caused by a stroke or by a series of mini-strokes. Symptoms are very similar to those for Alzheimer's disease, but often include walking difficulties, falling and changes to bladder function.

Fronto-temporal dementia is a result of changes to the frontal areas of the brain. Often, personality and behaviour changes, as well as self-neglect or craving sweet foods, are among the first noticeable symptoms with this type of dementia. Lots of people, however, will have a mixture of several types of dementia.

Other conditions that are associated with dementia but are less common include Lewy body dementia, Progressive Supranuclear Palsy (PSP) and Huntington's disease.

It has been estimated that there are 850,000 people

with dementia in the UK in 2015 and that this number will increase to 1 million by 2025. Dementia is more common in older age, but in fact can occur in people as young as forty.

What treatments are available for dementia?

At present, all drug treatments for dementia only slow down the progression and do not provide a cure. They are normally prescribed only for people in the earlier stages of Alzheimer's disease and not for those with other dementias. Many of the symptoms of dementia are made worse by stress, depression and physical problems such as infection, so it is important to seek advice from your GP about treatment for these symptoms if they occur.

People with a diagnosis of dementia are often seen for treatment and advice by a mental health team. This is not something to worry about; it is simply due to the fact that dementia services usually come under mental rather than physical health services in the NHS.

When dementia has been diagnosed

My relative has just been diagnosed with dementia

'*My husband has been forgetting things for over a year, but it was still a terrible shock when the doctor said that he thought it was dementia. I feel so afraid.*'
(*Mary, wife of someone newly diagnosed with Alzheimer's disease*)

A diagnosis of dementia is a shock both for the sufferer and for family and friends, even if it was half expected. God has created us as emotional beings who enjoy close relationships with other people, so, even as Christians, it is normal to experience negative emotions after a diagnosis. Common feelings include shock, sadness, confusion, anger, guilt and fear. Some people just feel numb at first. All these feelings are normal reactions to difficult news.

You will probably have lots of questions and concerns racing around in your mind for the first few days and weeks after diagnosis. As a result you may feel muddled and anxious. It may help to talk to someone and to share some of your feelings rather than trying to manage them on your own. You may have a supportive family member you can speak to; if not, your church leader or pastor should be willing to listen and support you as you find the emotional and practical help you need.

You may initially prefer to talk to someone anonymously, such as through the Samaritans or with someone from the Alzheimer's Society (see details at the end of this booklet). The important point is that you should not try to cope alone, as this will affect your own health. Give yourself time to process the initial shock; and expect to feel tearful, anxious, depressed and even angry or guilty for quite some time.

What do I need to do now?

> *'I still can't believe that Carol has been given a diagnosis of dementia. She's only*

just 65—we had so many plans.'
(Peter, husband of someone diagnosed
with vascular dementia)

The weeks and months following a diagnosis of dementia will feel very confusing for everyone. Be kind to yourself and take things slowly as you adjust to the news. While there is no hurry to sort out many things, there are a few practical aspects that do need to be dealt with as soon as possible:

Put everything in order

Make sure that any of your relative's important documents can easily be found, including details of the mortgage or tenancy agreement, insurance policies, bank statements or building society books. Sort out any recent bills, guarantees and regular payments. It might be a good idea to arrange for your loved one's regular household bills to be paid by direct debit.

Wills

Encourage your loved one to check that his or her will is up to date, or to consult a solicitor about making

17

a new one. Consider encouraging your relative to make an advance decision regarding what forms of treatment he or she would or would not like, in case such a decision becomes impossible to take in the future because of deteriorating health.

Arrange lasting power of attorney (LPA)

The person with dementia will need to grant lasting power of attorney to somebody he or she trusts. This enables someone else to manage his or her legal, financial and health affairs and to make decisions on his or her behalf should that become necessary. It is easiest if this person lives close to the dementia sufferer.

Work

If your loved one is still at work and finding it stressful, it may be good for him or her to find an opportunity to switch to a less demanding job or to reduce hours. Seek expert advice on pension rights if an occupational pension is due. Encourage your loved one not to rush into a resignation if he or she is still coping and enjoying work. Advise him or her to speak with the manager and the human resources department about the options for staying at work or leaving with the protection of the appropriate legislation. Before he or she leaves work, check whether there are benefits to which he or she may be entitled.

Driving

Many people can continue to drive after they have been diagnosed with dementia. Driving is a highly complex task involving coordination, vision, concentration and judgement—abilities that can all be affected by dementia—so you need to be sure that your relative is safe to drive. By law the DVLA and the insurance company must be informed of a diagnosis of dementia. Research has shown that relatives are often the most accurate judges of the standard of driving. If the person with dementia is still driving, make sure that someone goes with him or her as a passenger at least once a month to check that his or her driving performance is still at a safe level. If you are concerned, contact your GP or consultant for advice.

Support services

It will make things easier later if you know what services are available and how to access them before you actually need them. Contact your local Social Services department for details of services that they can arrange. You will find contact details listed in the phone book under the name of the County Council.

Find out what services can be arranged through your GP or consultant, and what kinds of services and support are provided by local voluntary organizations such as the Alzheimer's Society. Your local library and the Citizens Advice Bureau are good sources of information.

Register as a carer

Register yourself as a carer at your GP surgery as soon as possible, even if you are not yet providing care; this should mean that you will be given priority in terms of appointments and routine checks. Some GP practices offer support groups for people living with dementia and for their relatives. Find out about local services for carers so that they are known to you before you need them.

Contact the Alzheimer's Society

Contact details for the Alzheimer's Society are given at the end of this booklet. You can also find contact details for your local branch of the Alzheimer's

Society in the phone book or by asking at your local library. The Alzheimer's Society provides lots of information that will help you even if your loved one has another type of dementia.

The Alzheimer's Society will provide your relative with a 'help card'; this is a wallet-sized card to help explain dementia to anyone your relative might encounter in daily life and which is useful if he or she gets lost or needs help when alone.

Alcohol

It is fine for someone with dementia to drink alcohol, especially if it gives him or her pleasure, but encourage your loved one not to drink too much as it will increase disorientation. If your relative is taking medication, check with his or her doctor as to the amount of alcohol that can safely be consumed.

Medication

If your loved one is on medication, ask your GP to check whether this is essential, as it can sometimes increase confusion.

Health checks

Help your relative to keep up with routine checks. Poor vision and hearing can increase confusion. Encourage him or her to have regular eye and hearing checks as well as routine dental screening, as painful teeth, gums or dentures can make life more difficult.

Living with dementia

Be reassured: a diagnosis of dementia does not mean that this is the end of life for you or for your loved one. While dementia is a progressive disease, many people are now diagnosed early, and with a little planning it is possible to continue with previous activities and enjoy a good quality of life for quite some time after diagnosis.

Someone with dementia will need an increasing amount of help as the illness progresses, but it is important to make sure that other people don't take over when he or she is still capable of managing life. It is important that you discuss plans for the future with your loved one and with those who are closest to you.

The following suggestions will help you to enable your loved one retain his or her independence, sense of dignity and self-respect for as long as possible. You may find it useful to write down the ideas you think

23

are particularly important and give them to family, friends and people at church.

Telling others about the diagnosis

You may feel embarrassed or anxious about telling others that your family member has dementia. You may fear that your loved one will be treated differently or even be avoided by Christian friends. However, people are often simply afraid of saying or doing the wrong thing, so when you have found all the information you need and got over the initial shock, it will help them if you can tell them exactly what you and your relative need. Be as specific as possible.

Here are some examples:

- 'My husband gets muddled with the hymn numbers, may fall asleep in the service or even speak out of turn—but please keep talking to us anyway.'

- 'It would really help if sometimes she could sit next to someone else in church or during coffee time, so I can relax and have some fellowship time.'

- 'I would love someone to take him out once a week so I can have a bath, or for someone to sit with him while I pop to the shops.'

Often relatives worry about burdening others, even their Christian friends. It can feel difficult, but sharing problems is important for support. It might be useful to talk things through with your pastor so that he can speak to the right people and make sure you have people to support you. The Bible makes it clear that true Christians should be looking after each other:

> *Carry each other's burdens, and in this way you will fulfil the law of Christ.*
> *(Galatians 6:2)*

Communication

Ensure that your loved one is consulted on all matters that concern him or her. Help your relative to write down his or her wishes about things that are important while able to do so, and make sure that other people know what is important.

Discussions with your loved one will need to take

place more slowly than previously. Using a pen and paper to draw and write down key points will make difficulties with words and memory less of a problem. Your relative should have the opportunity to make his or her own choices for as long as possible.

People with dementia can find choice confusing, so keep things simple. Phrase questions so that they only need a 'yes' or 'no' answer; for example, ask 'Would you like to wear your blue jumper today?' rather than 'Which jumper would you like to wear today?'; 'Do you want coffee or tea?' rather than 'What would you like to drink?'

A person with dementia will understandably be sad or upset at times. In the earlier stages, he or she may want to talk about the anxieties and the problems he or she is experiencing. Try to understand how your loved one feels. Make time to offer support, rather than ignoring him or her or 'jollying him or her along'. Don't brush your loved one's worries aside, however painful or insignificant they may seem to be. If your loved one doesn't seem to be making sense, look for the meaning behind his or her words. Whatever the detail of what is said, your loved one is usually trying to communicate how he or she feels.

Everyday routines

Make time for occasional one-off visits or days out to make life interesting and enjoyable, but try to establish a daily and weekly routine that you stick to as much as possible. This will greatly help your relative as the condition progresses. As early as possible, build in regular exercise, which is known to be good for people with dementia and may keep mental abilities stable for longer. A short walk is sufficient. This will also help you to manage your own stress and anxiety. Use familiar routes so that your loved one can recognize where he or she is and feel safe.

Encourage your loved one to keep doing the activities he or she enjoys for as long as possible, even if more support will be needed. Although you may find it frustrating, it is important to let dementia sufferers do things at their own pace and in their own way as much as possible. Break activities down into small steps so that your relative can feel a sense of achievement, even if he or she can only manage part of a task. Do things *with* your loved one, rather than *for* him or her, to help him or her retain independence for as long as possible.

'Mary has always done the cooking, but now her memory and planning abilities

> *mean she can't do that alone. My daughter*
> *simplified her ten favourite recipes, printed*
> *them out, laminated them and put them*
> *in a folder in the kitchen. I cook any side*
> *dishes, but with these few changes Mary can*
> *feel she is still doing most of the cooking.'*
> (Peter, husband of someone with
> Alzheimer's dementia)

Avoid situations in which your relative is bound to fail, as this can be humiliating. Look for tasks that he or she can still manage and activities he or she enjoys.

Christian routines

Pray and read the Bible together, even if at times your relative does not appear able to process what is going on. These activities can only be positive, and the familiar routine will also be a comfort as the illness develops. You may have to make these times shorter as the illness progresses.

Ask your pastor or church leaders to help you and your loved one to keep going to church meetings. As the illness progresses, this may mean that other people will need to stay with your relative at home or in another part of the church so you can attend meetings and services, and continue to enjoy fellowship without the anxiety of caring for your loved one.

Relationships

In the early stages of the illness, your relative may lose confidence because of the difficulties encountered. Encourage him or her, when with other people, to ask questions, say that he or she has not understood, and not to be ashamed or afraid to admit that he or she has forgotten what has been said. Remind your loved one that it is not his or her fault that he or she can't remember as well as in the past.

Show affection to your loved one in a way you both feel comfortable with.

Make sure that others know how to help and support you so that they don't avoid your relative through fear of doing the wrong thing. Encourage close friends who have regular contact to make use of the resources at the end of this booklet so they have a fact-based understanding of dementia.

Encourage people to act with courtesy and kindness, however advanced the dementia. Never talk over your loved one's head as if he or she were not there, especially if you're talking about him or her.

When you are helping your relative, always explain what you are doing and why.

Make sure that your relative's right to privacy is respected. Ask others always to knock on the person's bedroom door before entering. If your loved one needs help with intimate personal care, such as washing or using the toilet, provide this help sensitively and make sure the door is kept closed if other people are around.

Managing cognitive problems

Cognitive problems include difficulties in areas such as memory, concentration, learning new things, mental arithmetic, reading and writing. Cognitive problems are often the first symptoms presented by people with dementia. In the early stages, many things can be done to make sure that these problems have less of an impact on everyday life and that your relative stays confident and independent for as long as possible. At the end of the booklet you will find details of a resource called 'Staying Smart', which is on the MS Trust website. This is actually designed for people with Multiple Sclerosis but it provides lots of ideas for managing cognitive problems that are also good for people with dementia. There are also tips for relatives, and details of various gadgets that can be purchased to help with practical problems such as getting lost and forgetting. Staying Smart is an online resource; if you don't have access to a computer, ask someone in your church to have a look and write down any ideas that would help your relative.

The following tips will help with some of the most common cognitive problems. Start putting them into practice as soon as possible so that they become habits:

- Put helpful telephone numbers by the phone where they can be seen.

- Put labels on cupboards or drawers as a reminder of where things are.

- Write reminders to lock the door at night or put out the rubbish on a certain day.

- Put items that are used frequently—such as a phone, keys or glasses—in an obvious place, such as a large bowl in the sitting room.

- Reduce distractions when your loved one needs to focus on something like eating, talking or reading. Turn off the radio or TV, and make sure that others in the room talk quietly or not at all.

- Build in rest times, as people with dementia become fatigued much more quickly; everyday activities require a lot more effort.

- Avoid having conversations in big groups; instead, encourage friends and family to visit one or two at a time.

- Use a simple scrapbook or photo album to record details of the past and present life of your loved one, including photos of key events and important family members and friends, newspaper cuttings and any other reminders. This is a nice activity that can be continued over time, and the resulting scrapbooks or albums are useful to have to hand when people visit, as they aid memory and conversation.

- Watch old movies or recordings of family events, and look at old photos. Long-term memory is frequently less affected, so encourage friends or family members to chat about things in the past. Your loved one will probably remember past events more clearly than recent events.

DON'T do activities like memory and word games to try to counteract the difficulties unless your loved one has always done that sort of thing and clearly enjoys them. Sometimes, relatives think that if they make their loved one try to remember or play memory games, it will help memory. This is not true. Often, memory is one of the first abilities to deteriorate; and making people do activities that place a high demand on short-term memory or on remembering words won't help but will rather make them feel sad and frustrated when they fail. It is a bit like insisting that someone in a wheelchair practises running to make his or her legs work.

Because of problems with attention, people with dementia may get muddled about who has done what and when, or may even say they have been involved in something they read or watched on TV. Try not to correct what the person says, even if you know it is not true. The accuracy of the information is not as important as what the person is trying to communicate.

Managing difficult behaviour

Sometimes, as the illness progresses, confusion and frustration can make people with dementia behave in ways that other people find irritating or upsetting.

> 'Peter has always been such a well-mannered person, but now, if he doesn't get what he wants straight away, he shouts and even swears at me. It is very hard as I so miss the man I married.'
>
> (Carol, married to someone with frontal temporal dementia)

Such behavioural changes include shouting, constant repetition, wandering, inappropriate urinating, and verbal or physical abuse. Try to remember that these difficulties are due to the dementia and are not personal or deliberate. If your loved one is being abusive, try to stay calm and, if possible, leave the room for a few minutes—at least until you feel calmer. Make use of Christian friends and ensure the church leaders organize at least two people you can call to come immediately if you feel unsafe or unable to cope.

Behavioural and personality changes can be the most challenging and upsetting symptoms of dementia for relatives. Make sure you ask for support from others as early as possible and that you get breaks away from your loved one at least on a weekly basis. Always share the problems with others and make sure that you keep yourself safe. Behavioural changes are no one's fault; they result from the changes in the brain produced by dementia.

Talking to children

It used to be believed that it was best for children if you kept difficulties hidden from them. It is now clear from research that children need to be told the facts in a way they can understand, as they quickly notice if something is wrong, and if they are not told about it, can become anxious and fearful. If the diagnosis is not discussed openly with children, there is good evidence to suggest that children will blame themselves for changes in their relative, or will worry that dementia might be catching.

Explain to children that your relative has something called 'dementia' and that this is the reason why he or she is behaving in an unusual way. Make the point more clearly by giving practical examples of behaviour that might seem strange, such as your relative forgetting where he or she is or wearing a hat in bed. Focus on the things that the person can still do, as well as those that are becoming more difficult.

Grandpa Seashells is a book for younger children that tells the story of some children and their grandfather who has dementia. At the back of the book are suggestions of things that children can still enjoy doing with a relative with dementia. The book is available from the Alzheimer's Society (details at the back of this booklet).

Explain to children how to use short, simple sentences giving cues and reminders that will help your relative know where he or she is and what is happening. For example, 'It's 12 o'clock, Grandma. You had a nice breakfast earlier—would you like a cup of tea now in the kitchen?' Encourage them to talk about old memories—for example, 'Do you remember when I fell out of a tree and you put a plaster on my leg?' Explain that your relative is understanding things more slowly and that they need to be patient. Tell them not to move suddenly as it may be frightening for our relative and he or she may then shout or lash out. Tell them not to argue with your relative, even if he or she is getting things wrong or muddled.

Caring for yourself

'In the early days we muddled through fine, but after several years I felt so tired. My husband was no longer the man I had married—he was always angry and unkind. At times, when he tried to lash out at me, I

felt I could have hit him back. I felt so alone and that I could no longer cope. In the end, I told someone at church how I was feeling and a rota was organized to help with meals and to give me breaks. I also found out that there was a carers group at my local community centre. I realized I wasn't alone. I wished I had asked for help so much earlier, as with a few regular breaks and some practical help I felt so much more like myself. I was able to see God's faithfulness again, and by his grace love my husband for who he was and not for what he used to be.'

(Maggie, wife of someone with Alzheimer's disease)

No temptation has overtaken you except what is common to mankind. And God is faithful; he will not let you be tempted beyond what you can bear. But when you are tempted, he will also provide a way out so that you can endure it.

(1 Corinthians 10:13)

The role of caring for someone with dementia can be difficult and challenging, not just physically, but emotionally too. Just as the individual with the diagnosis has to adjust to the challenges of the illness, so do you as a relative or friend.

Dealing with dementia is often referred to as a 'living bereavement' as you are facing the loss of the person you have known and loved, even though he or she is still alive. It is also normal to feel sad for the loss of the future you had planned together and the things that you had wanted to do but now may not be able to do. These feelings of loss are similar to the grief experienced after the death of a loved one and may include shock, sadness, despair, regret and even anger towards the person, other people and God.

Be reassured that all these feelings are normal. The important point is not to try to cope with it all on your own. Find people you can talk to honestly about your negative feelings. If you find talking to others difficult, keeping a journal of your thoughts and feelings may be helpful.

You may find yourself having to take on roles and tasks that you have never done before, such as cooking, managing money or driving. Write a list of all the things that need to be done and talk to your church leader, a friend or family member about who might be able to help with some of these tasks. Don't be tempted to try to do it all alone: getting help will mean that you will be able to cope with the caring role for longer.

It is vital to look after yourself because if you don't, your body or your mind will suffer, and then it will be much harder for both you and your relative. As soon as possible after the diagnosis, plan how you are going to look after yourself. Here are some ideas:

- Write a journal of how you are thinking and feeling, and of Bible verses that have encouraged or spoken to you. Writing a list of things for which you are grateful helps even in times of trouble. The Bible, of course, has much to say about being thankful in all things. Look up the following verses in your Bible and write them out in your journal: 1 Thessalonians 5:18; Psalm 107:1; and Philippians 4:6.

- Tell others what you need and ask your pastor or church leaders to enable you to get help and fellowship from others in the church and to continue to attend church meetings. Towards the end of this booklet is a sample letter to a church leader that may help you do this.

- Keep doing the things you enjoy. Again, ask people to help you with this through their spending time with your relative, thereby freeing you up.

- Look after your own physical health and don't be tempted to miss routine checks. If you become unwell, the situation will become much worse.

- Remind yourself that any behavioural problems your relative is showing are not your fault and are not intended to be personal, however it may feel.

- Talk to a close friend about how you are feeling so that you don't bottle up emotions like anger, distress and sadness and become depressed or overwhelmed.

- Be kind to yourself; don't say unkind things to yourself like, 'Why can't I cope? I'm terrible at this. If only people knew I shouted at him ...', and so on. Treat yourself as you would treat a Christian friend: be kind, and build in treats, relaxation time, and time with others who make you feel refreshed.

- As your relative becomes less independent, make sure that you are getting all the financial and practical help you are entitled to. Your GP will be a good starting point for advice.

Your local Social Services department can provide you with practical advice and support. They will help with things like:

- adapting your house or providing things like rails in the bathroom

- applications for financial support

- access to services like day centres and respite care when you need a break.

Sometimes, your feelings will reach a point where they become hard to manage and your usual ways of coping become less effective. It has been estimated that as many as three quarters of people who are caring for a close relative experience feelings of depression, anxiety or unmanageable stress at some point in their caring journey. People who have experienced anxiety or depression in the past are especially vulnerable. When you feel down or fearful more of the time than not, or if you begin to feel that you are unable to cope, it is vitally important that you tell someone. Talk to a close friend or a church leader; or you can contact your GP, who can put you in touch with someone to help you look at the difficulties and feelings you are experiencing. It may be that some medication would help.

The way you think about the difficulties you are facing will impact how you feel and cope. Living with someone with dementia is often a challenge, but that challenge can be made worse by the way we think about the situation. It is important to notice what thoughts you are listening to. Negative thoughts such as 'It's not fair! Why me? I can't cope! Where will this end?' are all common, but they make us feel sad, angry and upset, and often make us less able to cope. While you won't be able to rid yourself of these thoughts, it is important to notice them and try to focus on other things, rather than allow yourself to get trapped in a cycle of listening to these thoughts as if they are fact and then feeling hopeless. The Bible contains many verses that encourage us to think in a different way—for example:

> *Finally, brothers and sisters, whatever is true, whatever is noble, whatever is right, whatever is pure, whatever is lovely, whatever is admirable—if anything is excellent or praiseworthy—think about such things.*
> *(Philippians 4:8)*

It takes practice to do this as we are so easily hooked back into our old patterns of thoughts, but try to notice what you are thinking and whether or not it is helpful.

Why has God allowed this to happen to us?

When something upsetting happens it is natural to ask, 'Why me? Is it because of something I have done or not done?' If you are a Christian it is normal to ask why God has allowed someone in your family to be diagnosed with dementia. Sometimes, even Christian friends can make things worse with well-meaning comments about how we should cope or statements that might unintentionally imply blame, such as, 'Well, he has never liked exercise or healthy eating'; or 'He seems to have been in church less the last few years'; or even 'Perhaps this is a punishment for personal sin'.

So why does God allow suffering and disease in the world? What is the biblical perspective on why individuals suffer? And is there anything that can help Christians cope when life is not easy?

Is it wrong as a Christian to feel emotional pain in response to a situation?

The first important point to understand is that, sadly, suffering is a normal part of the human experience and as Christians we are not promised exemptions from it. The Bible consistently makes it clear that in fact, as Christians, we may even suffer more than most, due to our faith and consequential beliefs and behaviour.

The book of the Bible that makes clear many aspects of why Christians suffer and what helps is Job. Here we find described the life of a man considered upright and blameless; yet God allowed him to suffer more than most of us will ever have to endure. God allowed his property and his family to be destroyed and for Job to suffer intensely. Even Job's friends said unhelpful things, suggesting he was at fault and encouraging him to blame God.

> *For sighing has become my daily food;*
> *my groans pour out like water.*
> *What I feared has come upon me;*
> *what I dreaded has happened to me.*
> *I have no peace, no quietness;*
> *I have no rest, but only turmoil.*
> *(Job 3:24–26)*

45

The first thing to note is that, in response to the terrible things that were happening to him and his family, Job was hurting; he tore his clothes, shaved his head and sat in ashes. These were all public displays of his intense grief. He didn't feel pressured to put a smile on his face or claim that all was well when in fact it was not. He didn't deny his negative feelings or his pain. Suffering hurts, and God does not blame us for feeling or expressing the pain. This pain is a normal human response to distressing things, including when a loved one receives a frightening diagnosis like dementia. We have been created as emotional beings, and as Christians God doesn't ask us to suppress or hide our pain from him or from others.

Is dementia due to personal sin?

The Bible makes it clear that, as human beings, we are all born sinful and that we are living in a fallen world that includes disease and sadness. In Romans 8 Paul says that the whole of creation is groaning under the weight of sin and judgement. From the moment Adam disobeyed God in Genesis 3, sin became part of every human who was born. This means that our human nature is a sinful nature. Sometimes people do suffer directly because of the consequences of their sinful actions. For example, if someone drives when drunk and kills someone, that driver will suffer anguish and probably be put in prison. If a man is unfaithful to his wife, he will probably experience a great deal of personal and family suffering as a result.

However, the Bible makes it clear that suffering in general is not a punishment for personal sin. In the opening verse of Job it is immediately clear that Job did not experience his later suffering as a result of his sin. Job 1:1 says,

> *In the land of Uz there lived a man whose*
> *name was Job. This man was blameless and*
> *upright; he feared God and shunned evil.*

In John 9 the disciples asked Jesus if a man was born blind because of his or his parents' sin. Jesus replied,

> *Neither this man nor his parents sinned ...*
> *but this happened so that the works of God*
> *might be displayed in him. (v. 3)*

This verse says that sometimes we suffer so that God can be seen in our situation. C. S. Lewis said, 'God whispers to us in our pleasures, speaks in our conscience, but shouts in our pains: it is his

47

megaphone to rouse a deaf world.'[1] Perhaps our neighbours will notice that we are still trusting God despite our pain; perhaps our non-Christian friends will be encouraged and challenged by how faithful our church and Christian friends are in helping us. Most often, however, we have no idea why we are experiencing suffering and we simply have to trust in the truth of God's promise that 'in all things [he] works for the good of those who love him' (Romans 8:28), even when we don't understand.

At the end of the book of Job we see that, despite what he went through, Job trusted God more than ever, even though he never knew the purpose of his suffering. Often, Christians testify that it is the hard times that result in a deepening of their faith. This is certainly what we are promised in Romans 5:3–5:

> ... *we know that suffering produces perseverance; perseverance, character; and character, hope. And hope does not put us to shame, because God's love has been poured out into our hearts through the Holy Spirit, who has been given to us.*

---

1 C. S. Lewis, *The Problem of Pain*; cited at http://www.goodreads.com/work/quotes/2976220-the-problem-of-pain; accessed May 2015.

This verse makes it clear that it is suffering and not the easy times that develop our Christian character, and that we won't be disappointed by what God does in our lives.

When suffering comes, it can be a true test of our faith and whether that faith is Bible based. Job asked,

Shall we accept good from God, and not trouble?
(Job 2:10)

If our faith holds true only when life is easy, it is not a true or biblical faith. We mostly don't have any choice about how or when we suffer, but with God's grace we can choose our response to our suffering. We can trust his Word that says that, while suffering may not be our fault, it can result in our good; or we can blame God and push him away—and in so doing feel more desolate than ever.

Is my relative still a Christian even if he or she is behaving in a way that is not consistent with the Christian faith?

The thought that a relative with dementia might no longer be—and never was—a Christian because of his or her dementia-related behaviour is a common

49

anxiety for Christian family members and a misunderstanding that is sometimes found within Christian communities. It is sometimes even implied that the dementia-related symptoms of difficult behaviour or unkind words are due to unconfessed or unforgiven sin.

The Bible tells us that, when someone recognizes and repents of his or her sin in the light of what Jesus has completed on the cross, that person can be assured of sins forgiven and the presence of the Holy Spirit dwelling in him or her for ever. When we confess our sin,

> ... [God] is faithful and just and will forgive us
> our sins and purify us from all unrighteousness.
> (1 John 1:9)

The forgiveness that the Bible talks about for believers is total, a change of status in God's eyes. Because of what Jesus has done on the cross, God can look on us sinners and see the righteousness of Jesus instead of our sin. Thus, when we become Christians, we are born again: our past, present and future sin is all forgiven in that moment. Once someone has been truly born again, that person can't be 'unborn', in the same way that, once a baby is born, that change in status from baby in the womb to baby post-birth cannot be reversed, whether by that baby's will or by the will of another. Those who view abnormal behaviour in dementia patients as related to unforgiven sin diminish the work of the cross.

Our physical bodies are dying from the moment we are born. Body parts wear out and contract disease, and the ageing process can't be halted. The Bible refers to our bodies as 'the earthly tent' (2 Corinthians 5:1). Our brains are also part of our physical bodies and of this earthly tent. Physical health problems like arthritis impact our physical abilities, whereas dementia destroys different parts of the brain and thus produces reduced control over both physical and mental abilities.

As human beings, we hear and see many things in our lives that our brains absorb without us even processing them. For dementia sufferers, the control that they have over what they say and do is diminished; thus men and women who have always behaved in a godly manner may suddenly behave and speak in ways that are inconsistent with their previous Christian character—all because of the dementia.

However, the Bible reassures us that, even though our bodies and minds fade, our heavenly status remains the same, and in heaven we will have new bodies that will not be vulnerable to disease:

> *For we know that if the earthly tent we live in is destroyed, we have a building from God, an eternal house in heaven, not built by human hands.*
>
> *(2 Corinthians 5:1)*

In the meantime, even when a Christian is humanly unrecognizable due to dementia, his or her spirit is intact and being comforted by the Holy Spirit in a way we can't understand. Your loved one's position as a Christian is secure. Romans 8:38–39 promises us that nothing can separate us from God's love, and that includes dementia:

> *For I am convinced that neither death nor life, neither angels nor demons, neither the present nor the future, nor any powers, neither height nor depth, nor anything else in all creation, will be able to separate us from the love of God that is in Christ Jesus our Lord.*

A final note

If your relative has dementia—especially if it is your husband or your wife—it can feel very lonely. It is normal to miss the company and intimacy that you previously shared as a couple and to feel very alone. However, if you are a Christian you are never alone. We have been promised constant comfort through the presence of the Holy Spirit; and of course Jesus knows what it is like to suffer and to feel completely alone. As Christians we are not given all the answers, but we are promised the constant presence of the one who has all the answers. Be assured that, even when friends, family members and fellow Christians let you down, God will never leave you or forsake you.

I close with what has become my favourite verse in times of distress:

> *For I am the LORD your God*
> *who takes hold of your right hand*
> *and says to you, Do not fear;*
> *I will help you.*
>
> *(Isaiah 41:13)*

LETTER TO A CHURCH LEADER

This is a letter that you could give to leaders in your church to enable them to understand your situation. It doesn't describe all that the church leaders need to know, but it may help you to start a conversation about what support you might need in the coming months.

Dear Church Leader,

We hope this might give you an idea of how to ensure that the person giving you this letter gets good support from the leaders and congregation at their church following a diagnosis of dementia in their family.

If the diagnosis of dementia is new, the whole family will experience days and weeks of feelings of distress and fear. At this time the relatives and the dementia sufferer will most of all need Christian people to listen to them without judgement and without trying to solve the situation or think of things to say. There is very little that can be said apart from to reassure them that what they are feeling is understandable and that you, as a church, will ensure that both emotional and practical support will be readily available. Pray with and for the family for comfort for all and that they will know God's grace in their lives; and encourage other people within the church to continue to pray, even if the family can no longer play as active a part in church as previously.

It would be helpful if you could continue to pray with the dementia sufferer if he or she will accept that. Keep prayers short and simple. Play or sing familiar music or hymns, and continue to refer to your faith in Jesus, the Bible, and the hope we have of heaven and a new body when this life is tough and our bodies are failing.

There are certain practical things that need to be sorted out fairly urgently—such as getting the dementia sufferer's affairs in order, and sorting out work, driving and a lasting power of attorney. It might be helpful at this point if the person or relative is encouraged to write a list of what needs to be done and, if appropriate, you could arrange for someone from the church to provide support in finding out the appropriate information and working through the list.

Every situation is different, but it would then be useful to help the relative think about who in the church can be a good support now and in the future. There may also be people the relative doesn't want to be involved. If your congregation is big enough, it might be useful to get together a small group that can be given the task of supporting the dementia sufferer and his or her relative both inside and outside church. Dementia is increasingly common, and churches need to be able to support people who are touched by this disease.

In the early stages, the relative or person with dementia may just want a weekly or monthly telephone contact or visit; a listening ear is often the most useful thing that can be offered.

*As the disease progresses, it would
probably be useful if the relative has a list
of church members who can be called on
to help with different things; even older
teens can do shopping, change light bulbs
or do light cleaning. Older church members
can be called on for emotional support,
transport to appointments, cleaning,
cooking, and so on. Make sure the people
know as much as possible about the person
with dementia, especially his or her life
histories and his or her likes and dislikes.
Please remind people always to speak with
respect to the person with dementia as an
individual created in God's image, even if he
or she is no longer able to communicate his
or her needs. Encourage others to make eye
contact and to speak clearly without being
patronizing or as if the dementia sufferer is
a child.*

*Of course, the specific help given needs
to be discussed and agreed with the family,
but often people say they are afraid to ask
and don't know what help to request. If
help is not forthcoming in the early phase,
relatives frequently become too stressed or*

low in the later phases to know what they need or to ask for help.

If the person with dementia starts to present difficult behaviour, ensure there are always at least two people who can be called at any time of day or night and without an explanation. These people need to know that if a call is made, help is needed, and their response should be just to go. This group needs to be helped to know how to respond to difficult behaviour. There is lots of information on this and many other practical issues in the booklet *Help! Someone I Love Has Dementia*.

Encourage the relative to look after him- or herself and to keep up with his or her own life without feeling guilty. Acknowledge the grief that he or she is feeling even though his or her loved one is still alive, and help him or her still to be able to attend church meetings by arranging others to sit with the person with dementia at home or in church so that the relative can enjoy fellowship without anxiety.

What an amazing witness it would be if a cynical world of neighbours and health and social care professionals could see how God's people respond to families affected by dementia!

Where can I get further help?

Books

Baxendale, Dr Sallie, *Coping with Memory Problems* (London: Sheldon Press, 2014). This book can help you if you are worried about memory but a diagnosis hasn't been made.

Johnson, Jo, *Grandpa Seashells* (London: Speechmark Publishing, 2013). This is a story book for children aged 3 to 11. It tells the story of a family who have a grandfather with dementia. Available on Amazon or from the Alzheimer's Society.

Morse, Louise, and Roger Hitchings, *Could It Be Dementia? Losing Your Mind Doesn't Mean Losing Your Soul* (Oxford: Monarch, 2008). This is an excellent resource for Christians who have friends or relatives with dementia or for anyone who wants to know how better to support others affected by dementia.

Useful organizations and websites

These organizations provide accurate information about dementia and about where help can be found. If you don't use a computer, ask your church leader or younger family members to help you find what you need.

Age UK:
www.ageuk.org.uk

Alzheimer's Society:
www.alzheimers.org.uk

Carers Christian Fellowship:
www.carerschristianfellowship.org

Carers UK:
www.carersuk.org

Carers Trust:
www.carers.org

Pilgrim Homes:
www.pilgrimhomes.org.uk

Staying Smart:
www.stayingsmart.org.uk

Booklets in the *Help!* series include ...

HELP! I can't submit to my husband (GLENDA HOTTON)
ISBN 978-1-84625-321-8

HELP! I feel ashamed (SUE NICEWANDER)
ISBN 978-1-84625-320-1

HELP! I have breast cancer (BRENDA FRIELDS)
ISBN 978-1-84625-216-7

HELP! I'm living with terminal illness (REGGIE WEEMS)
ISBN 978-1-84625-319-5

HELP! I've been deployed (RODDY MACLEOD)
ISBN 978-1-84625-459-8

HELP! My baby has died (REGGIE WEEMS)
ISBN 978-1-84625-215-0

HELP! My toddler rules the house (PAUL & KAREN TAUTGES)
ISBN 978-1-84625-221-1

HELP! Someone I love has been abused (JIM NEWHEISER)
ISBN 978-1-84625-222-8

HELP! Someone I love has dementia (JO JOHNSON)
ISBN 978-1-84625-458-1

HELP! Someone I love has depression (JIM WINTER)
ISBN 978-1-84625-460-4